Designing for health and safety in construction

A guide for designers on the Construction
(Design and Management) Regulations 1994

HSE BOOKS

This is guidance prepared, in consultation with the Health and Safety Executive, by the Construction Industry Advisory Committee which was appointed by the Health and Safety Commission as part of its formal advisory structures. The guidance represents what is considered to be good practice by the members of the Committee. It has been agreed by the Commission. Following this guidance is not compulsory and you are free to take other action. But if you do follow this guidance you will normally be doing enough to comply with the law. Health and safety inspectors seek to secure compliance with the law and may refer to this guidance as illustrating good practice.

This text was prepared by CONIAC with the help and advice of Sylvester Bone BA, RIBA, AAdip, Dip TP, FASI.

Contents

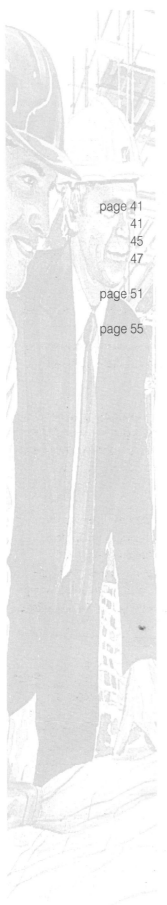

Introduction

1   This book provides guidance on the Construction (Design and Management) Regulations 1994 (CDM) for designers involved in construction work. The CDM Regulations are needed because of the unacceptably high rate of death, injury and ill health associated with all types of project ranging from new works through to subsequent maintenance, repair, refurbishment and eventual demolition. The Regulations have an impact on all stages of the planning and management of health and safety of a project. They place duties on clients, designers and construction organisations and introduce two new roles to the procurement process: the planning supervisor and the principal contractor. There are also new documents - health and safety plans and the health and safety file.

2   The Regulations are supported by an Approved Code of Practice (ACoP). This book should be read in conjunction with the ACoP. It sets out the duties placed upon designers by the Regulations and introduces the duties of the other parties to the procurement process as they relate to designers. A number of terms used in the book are defined by the Regulations. In any cases of doubt the meaning ascribed by the Regulations should be assumed. To assist those new to the health and safety field, a glossary of terms is included at the back of this publication.

3   The Regulations give the terms design and designer a wide definition and cover all designs and specifications to be used for the purposes of construction and all those involved in their preparation. The Regulations relate to all designs. Designers should now pay adequate regard to health and safety risks when considering their designs.

4   Designs develop from initial concepts through to a detailed specification. Different teams and individuals are involved at various stages. At each stage designers from all disciplines have a contribution to make in avoiding and combating health and safety risks in construction. At various stages within the design process different mixes of design disciplines may be involved. For example, architects may produce a concept which is then developed in detail by a combined team from architectural and engineering disciplines. The development of the detailed specification may then depend on a range of specialist teams.

5   At the concept stage fundamental decisions about the design are taken. Some of these decisions will affect construction health and safety, for example the location of the structure on the site. As the design evolves decisions taken at early stages in the design process may be influenced by later decisions, such as the arrangement for fixing curtain walling. During detailed specification, decisions will be taken which can further influence health and safety, for example the solvent content of glues and adhesives to be used for fixings.

6   This book outlines the broad principles of designing for health and safety. Designers should consider these principles and apply them to the particular design process for which they are responsible. It is the application of the principles set out in this book which presents designers with the opportunity to contribute to an improvement in health and safety standards in the industry.

7   This book also gives examples of health and safety hazards associated with various types of work. Considering such hazards as part of the design process may be new to some designers. Some might need to obtain more knowledge or discuss their designs with contractors, or specialists, more than they have before, so that they can fulfil their CDM duties. What is important is that their approach to solving design problems involves a proper exercise of judgement which takes account of health and safety issues.

8   As the design professions become more skilled in health and safety matters, the standard by which the exercise of proper judgement will be evaluated will increase. Therefore individual designers and design teams will need to take steps to review the health and safety knowledge and procedures they bring to bear on projects and evaluate their performance against that of other design professionals.

9   The matters addressed by the book relate to the design process and the relationship between designers and others with health and safety duties in the construction phase. The Regulations do not place extra duties on designers in relation to the on-site management of health and safety during the construction phase of a project.

How designers can contribute to health and safety

10   Those who spend their working lives on construction sites have a 1 in 300 chance of being killed at work. The chance of being disabled by injury or serious illness is much greater than for workers in most other industrial sectors. Every construction worker is likely to be temporarily unfit to work at some time as a result of a less serious injury or health problem after working on a construction site. Construction work also kills, injures and causes ill health for members of the public. The statistics have improved in recent years but they still not only represent tragedy and hardship for those involved and for their families, but also an enormous waste of resources (8.5% of construction costs in one HSE study, *The costs of accidents at work* (see page 55)). Tables 1 and 2 show the most common causes of death and injury (see pages 4 and 5). Table 3 shows some of the serious health hazards in construction (see page 6).

Workers are over five times more likely to be killed on a construction site than in a factory.

11   Accidents and ill health result from a combination of circumstances, some of which are related to design. Often several factors contribute to a single incident. Responsibility for each factor may be traced to a different individual or organisation. The work itself may have involved an unnecessary risk, there may have been insufficient protection or training and the injured person may have been careless. In such cases no one is wholly to blame but more attention to health and safety by any one of those responsible might have avoided the particular combination of circumstances - and there would have been no accident.

Although many may share the blame for an accident, any one of them could have made its occurrence less likely.

12   Legislation has been used to raise standards in other areas of design such as: energy conservation, the environmental impact of major projects and access for the disabled. It is now being used to ensure that designers pay more attention to health and safety. While aspects of site safety such as stability during construction, the safety of the public and safe access for maintenance have been regularly considered in design, few designers have carried out the systematic and routine reviews of the safety aspects of their designs which the CDM Regulations imply. Under the CDM Regulations designers of building, civil engineering and engineering construction work have specific duties, which are explained in this book.

Designers already have to strike a balance between different requirements, many of which are backed by legislation. The safety of construction workers is being brought into that balance with the duties placed on designers by the CDM Regulations. Designers should make their contribution to improving health and safety on site through the project design and planning process. Designers are not being given any additional responsibilities for the management of site activities; this remains the responsibility of the contractors.

Why do some risks go unrecognised?

13   The risks in certain types of construction work have become widely recognised. Designers have accepted, as a matter of course, that certain types of work must be designed, specified and costed to take account of essential precautions. They have accepted that operations such as motorway repair, removal of asbestos insulation or the demolition of a tall structure require careful planning. However, the risks in other types of work have been less widely appreciated and the opportunities to reduce those risks at the design stage have not been generally acknowledged. Normal practice (in building especially) has been for designers to leave many health and safety issues to contractors, so consequently the opportunities to reduce risks at the design stage have been lost. The first step designers can take is to recognise the risks involved in construction work.

Jobs that designers have already recognised as dangerous are not the only ones that cause deaths, injuries and health problems.

Common causes of death and serious injury

Table 1   Processes with the most reported injuries and fatalities

Process	Total of reported non-fatal injuries and (fatalities) 1993/4p*
Finishing/plastering/glazing	5745 (6)
Transfer of people/materials (on site)	2186 (8)
Surfacing: paving/road laying	1573 (3)
Groundworks: excavation/sewers	1428 (7)
Handling	1345
Loading/unloading	1154 (1)
Labouring	868
Bricklaying	789 (2)
Structural erection	722 (3)
Scaffolding	663 (3)
Maintaining: repair/renovation	434 (2)

*p = provisional

Table 2 1993/94p* Fatal injuries to employees and the self-employed in the construction sector as reported to HSE's Field Operations Division Inspectorates

Type of accident	Number of fatalities	Percentage of total
FALLS FROM A HEIGHT		
Ladders (all types)	9	
Scaffolding (all types)	8	
Fragile roofs	8	
Roof edges or holes in roofs	6	
Structural steelwork	4	
Temporary work platform (above ground)	3	
Parts of floors/surfaces not listed above	4	
Other	1	
Total	**43**	**56%**
TRAPPED BY SOMETHING COLLAPSING OR OVERTURNING		
Buildings/structures (or parts of)	7	
Earth, rocks eg trench collapse	3	
Plant including lifting machinery	1	
Scaffolding collapse	1	
Vehicles falling from supports/ overturning	3	
Other	1	
Total	**16**	**21%**
STRUCK BY A MOVING VEHICLE		
Bulldozer	1	
Excavator	2	
Private vehicle	1	
Road tanker	1	
Trailer	1	
Other	2	
Total	**8**	**10%**
CONTACT WITH ELECTRICITY OR AN ELECTRICAL DISCHARGE		
Domestic type equipment	1	
Hand tools or hand lamps	1	
Overhead lines	2	
Total	**4**	**5%**
STRUCK BY A FALLING/FLYING OBJECT DURING MACHINE LIFTING OF MATERIALS		
Total	**3**	**4%**
CONTACT WITH MOVING MACHINERY OR MATERIAL BEING MACHINED		
Conveyor belt	1	
Hoist	1	
Total	**2**	**3%**
EXPOSURE TO A HOT OR HARMFUL SUBSTANCE		
Total	**1**	**1%**

*p = provisional

Examples of health hazards in construction

Table 3 Annual estimates of numbers suffering from work-related ill health in the construction industry (95% confidence limit)

	Potential numbers suffering			
Hazard	**Possible resulting disease or condition**	**Estimated lower limit**	**Estimated upper limit**	**Ref source**
Asbestos	Mesothelioma Asbestosis Lung cancer	200-250 deaths* 100 cases** At least 200-250 deaths***		ARSS
Musculoskeletal injury	Total	30,400	48,100	LFS
	[Back disorders	14,700	27,800]	
	Work Related Upper Limb Disorders (WRULD)	4,600	13,000	
	Lower limb disorders	1,100	6,500	
	Unspecified musculoskeletal	3,800	11,700]	
Respiratory Disease	Lower Respiratory Disease (bronchitis, emphysema etc)	2,000	8,500	LFS
	Asthma	1,000	5,800	
	Pneumoconiosis (excluding asbestos)	300	4,400	
	Upper Respiratory Disease (sinusitis, influenza etc)	300	4,400	
Skin disease	Dermatitic conditions	3,100	10,500	LFS
Noise	Deafness and ear conditions (Tinnitus)	1,000	5,800	LFS
Ionising radiations	Radiation exposure	50 (exposed to more than 15mSv)		CIDI ARSS
Lead	Lead poisoning	18 (above suspension level of 69ug/100ml)		ARSS
Compressed air	Decompression sickness	50		HSE

Reference Source List

Key:

ARSS 1993/94 HSC Annual Report Statistical Supplement

LFS 1990 Labour Force Survey

CIDI 1986-1991 Analysis of doses reported to the Health and Safety Executive Central Index of Dose Information

HSE HSE estimate (from HSE tunnelling expert)

NB: Evidence from the supplementary 'Trailer' questionnaire to the Employment Department 1990 LFS indicates that the true annual prevalence for the occupational ill health categories identified above among people working in construction operations during the three years prior to Spring 1990 is likely to lie between the lower and upper limits quoted.

*   Based on last full time occupation recorded on 1991 death certificates

**   Same proportion as above applied to disablement benefit cases

*** Based on mesothelioma death certificate proportion

14   Design defines the work to be done. Designers may be the only people able to make the decision that will eliminate a foreseeable risk. For example, the designers may:

- be able to determine the location of the structure on the site. The location affects how close construction plant, eg piling rigs, cranes etc has to come to railway lines, roads and overhead power lines. Risks arising in this way can be influenced by the designer;

- select a type of window that can be cleaned from the inside;

- specify that blocks under 20 kg should be used, to reduce manual handling problems.

Obviously more is required than merely adopting such solutions as may occur to designers. There needs to be a systematic approach if health and safety is to be treated properly as a design consideration. For instance, an option that avoids one danger might introduce others. The designer then has to assess the risks of the alternatives.

15   At the outset designers should aim to:

(a) identify the significant health and safety hazards likely to be associated with the design and how it may be constructed and maintained;

(b) consider the risk from those hazards which arise as a result of the design being incorporated into the project under consideration;

(c) if possible, alter the design to avoid the risk or where this is not reasonably practicable follow the remainder of the hierarchy of risk control.

Designers should be aware of the hierarchy of risk control which underlies the modern approach to health and safety management - it is best to prevent the hazard and alter the design to avoid the risk. If this is not reasonably practicable the risk should be combated at source (eg ensure the design details of items to be lifted include lifting attachments). Failing this, priority should be given to controls that will protect all workers (eg arrange the design to allow the early installation of stairways into the new structure, allow for a one-way system for delivery and spoil removal vehicles etc). Only then should personal protection of individuals (eg harnesses, respirators etc) be assumed.

Designers should systematically exercise the health and safety issues associated with their designs. When they recognise a risk they may be able to avoid it altogether - often no one else can.

16   Health and safety needs to be considered at the same time as other design issues. The safest option is not always practicable because of other considerations. The aim should be to select a design option that entails fewer foreseeable risks, within the limits of what is reasonably practicable. The designer should look for ways of reducing and controlling the risks that remain. For example:

- piecemeal construction required at high level may be designed to be prefabricated at ground level, therefore reducing the risk of serious falls;

- non-toxic chemicals of comparable performance may be used in many situations, but if this is not possible, potentially toxic chemicals can be specified to be supplied in a diluted form;

- ample space can be allowed for the maintenance and replacement of equipment to reduce the likelihood of back strain and other injury from manual handling and lifting operations.

To make these judgements in the systematic way already described, designers need to adopt risk assessment - this is a common sense procedure and its significance is explained in more detail later. Practical guidance is given in Section 5.

How far are designers expected to go in reducing risk?

17 The duties on designers when considering health and safety in their design work are qualified by:

(a) what is reasonable for a designer to do at the time the design is prepared; and

(b) by what is reasonably practicable.

In determining (b), the risk to health and safety produced by a feature of the design has to be weighed against the cost of excluding that feature by following the hierarchy of risk control.

18 The cost is counted not just in financial terms but also those of fitness for purpose, aesthetics, buildability or environmental impact. The overall design process does not need to be dominated by a concern to avoid all risks during the construction phase and subsequent maintenance. By applying these principles it may be possible to make decisions at the design stage which will avoid or reduce risks during construction work. In many cases, the large number of design considerations will allow a number of equally valid design solutions. What is important is that the approach to solving design problems involves a proper exercise of judgement which takes account of health and safety issues.

19 If, after consideration, it is not reasonably practicable to avoid the risks to health and safety due to buildability, aesthetic or other factors, sufficient information will need to be provided about the risks which remain. This information needs to be included with the design to alert others to the risks which they cannot reasonably be expected to know about.

There will always be health and safety risks on construction sites - but designers are in a good position to reduce unnecessary levels of risk.

What health and safety information should the design take account of?

20 A designer's work involves gathering information about:

(a) the site, including topography, ground conditions and environment;

(b) existing and neighbouring structures;

(c) products and materials;

(d) the operation of construction plant and equipment;

(e) the operation of fixed plant and equipment.

The work also involves adopting design principles and assumptions. The designer should see that information about risks is stated to the extent necessary to enable reliable performance by a competent contractor.

> *Design documents that tell a contractor what has to be done also need to include information on hazards which are not immediately obvious.*

1

Designers' duties

21   Under the CDM Regulations designers have a duty to ensure that their designs pay adequate regard to health and safety - foreseeable risks should be avoided. If it is not reasonably practicable to avoid them they should be reduced and controlled.

Key points

22   There are four aspects of these Regulations that all designers need to appreciate before going into detail:

(a)   The CDM Regulations are not like building regulations or the Department of Transport specifications. There are no approvals or technical requirements. These Regulations place a duty on designers to consider the health and safety of people affected by the work - and they explain which measures should be given priority.

(b)   It is not only designers who have duties under the CDM Regulations. Duties are placed on all those in charge of the construction process, whether they are clients, contractors or subcontractors. For example, one of the client's duties is to appoint a planning supervisor to co-ordinate the health and safety aspects of project design and planning.

(c)   Operating the CDM Regulations is a collaborative effort. The Regulations only become effective when people work together to tackle health and safety risks. Whatever confrontation occurs in relation to other aspects of a project, when it comes to health and safety all parties have a duty to co-operate and have to pass on relevant information.

(d)   Designers' duties apply whatever size or type of construction work is involved. Many aspects of the CDM Regulations do not apply to very small jobs and some do not apply to work for clients on their own houses, but the Regulation defining the designers' duties always applies (except for some generally minor and interior work, where the local authority is the health and safety enforcing authority, and so CDM does not apply).

Who are the designers?

23   The term 'designer' has a very broad meaning in the Regulations. It includes:

■   architects and engineers contributing to, or having overall responsibility for, the design;

■   building services engineers designing details of fixed plant;

■   surveyors specifying articles or substances or drawing up specifications for remedial works;

■   contractors carrying out design work as part of a design and build project;

■   anyone with authority to specify, or alter the specification of designs to be used for the structure;

■   temporary works engineers designing formwork and falsework; and

■   interior designers, shopfitters and landscape architects.

The 'designer' may be an individual, partnership or a firm employing a number of designers. The process of design covered by the Regulations relates to the design of new structures and the specification and design of remedial and improvement work to existing structures. Responsibility for design may extend from those engineers and architects who traditionally think of themselves as design professionals to employees of construction companies (eg temporary works engineers) who have not previously considered themselves as designers. For example, a structural engineer may design a building's frame. The design may include information about requirements for temporary support, loads the temporary support needs to withstand and erection sequence. A temporary works engineer employed by a contractor may then be responsible for the detail temporary works design. Both designers have duties to consider health and safety.

24 Designers, through their designs, play a vital part in reducing hazards on a site and during subsequent maintenance and repair works. Control of risk on site is the responsibility of contractors. However, the designer 'sets the scene' and by considering hazards in a structured way can avoid or reduce risks and make subsequent control easier. Designers are required by the Regulations to apply the hierarchy of risk control, as already explained.

Avoiding risks

25 Designers should avoid foreseeable risks, eg by selecting non-fragile roofing materials, or by avoiding the disturbance of contaminated land.

What if risks cannot be avoided?

26 If risks cannot be avoided, they should be combated at source so far as reasonably practicable, eg by specifying brush application of a treatment rather than spraying, to reduce solvent exposure or by specifying a finishing material containing less harmful constituents.

What is meant by control of risk?

27 Measures which protect everyone should be given priority over those which protect only an individual. Often, only the contractor can select the right measure, eg local exhaust ventilation in preference to personal protective equipment. However, if the designer is in a position to influence control methods, these principles should be adopted, eg fixed rails on a maintenance walkway rather than relying on safety harnesses.

> *It is the designer's duty to see if hazards can be avoided; and if they cannot, to look for ways of combating the risk at source and of providing general rather than individual protection.*

Design information and co-operation

What sort of information does the designer need to pass on?

28 The other duties placed on designers relate to:

(a) the provision of information about aspects of the design that might affect health and safety of people on site (or affected by the works);

(b) co-operation with other designers and with the planning supervisor;

(c) the provision of information for inclusion in the health and safety file.

This might include:

- highlighting the need to provide guarded access routes when servicing or replacing roof level equipment if there is a danger of falling through the roof, eg if the roof is made of fragile material;

- ensuring that relevant information is provided about a cantilevered slab where work carried out without additional support might lead to its collapse;

- passing on information that could affect the safety of future alteration or demolition of a structure, eg where pre-stressed structural members exist or the location of services.

29   Where basic design assumptions affect health or safety, or health and safety risks are not obvious from the standard design documents, the designer should provide additional information. The information should include a broad indication of the designer's assumptions about the precautions which will be taken by the contractor to deal with the risks. An unusual design may require particular attention by the contractor when considering the detailed method of construction. The designer should make clear the principles of the design and describe any special requirements for the purposes of construction.

30   As a general rule of thumb, sufficient information should be included with the design to alert others to the risks within the design. This should include information which they cannot reasonably be expected to know. Risks have to be stated only to the extent necessary to enable a competent contractor to properly identify and assess the risks and put appropriate precautions in place.

How should designers record the decisions they make about health and safety?

31   The Regulations do not specifically require designers to keep a record of the design decisions they made and how they took account of health and safety when they made their decisions. However, designers may need to assure the planning supervisor that health and safety was given adequate regard among the other design considerations. Where quality assurance schemes are already in use to track other design decision-making processes, they may provide a suitable framework for controlling and monitoring the CDM decision-making process.

32   However, many designers do not use formalised quality assurance procedures. The mechanisms they already use to ensure they have considered all relevant aspects of a design at critical stages of its development (eg checklists or design review meetings), may provide a suitable framework for taking account of CDM decisions. Other systems may be developed by designers which could be equally satisfactory. As experience with CDM grows within the design professions, the systems most appropriate for monitoring CDM-related design decisions will become apparent. Whatever systems are developed they should integrate easily into the design process. Also, they should record only key information and avoid unnecessary bureaucracy.

What benefits does recording health and safety considerations have?

33   A formal system which produces an auditable trail through the stages of design development will assist the designer in demonstrating competence and adequate resourcing when tendering for work. Recording health and safety decisions will aid designers in controlling the CDM decision-making process. It can also lead to a more consistent approach to the consideration of health and safety in design. The consistent recording and reviewing of health and safety issues will also help make sure that decisions are taken when design options are still open. Issues raised at earlier stages can be revisited in the light of more recent design decisions. Additional aspects of health and safety that only become apparent as the design is developed can also be incorporated in this way. Structuring the collection of health and safety information will also assist its effective passage to the planning supervisor.

34   The duty to co-operate with other designers and the planning supervisor includes, for instance:

- exchanging drawings, design information and assumptions between separately commissioned designers of related aspects of a project;

- agreeing acceptable access arrangements for services in ducts and above ceilings;

- providing the planning supervisor with details of health and safety issues raised at design reviews, and with safety data sheets for hazardous materials specified.

The amount of interchange of information and co-operation with other designers and the planning supervisor required will vary from project to project.

It is the designer's duty to provide information on those aspects of design which others might not reasonably be expected to know and to co-operate with the other designers and with the planning supervisor.

Competence and resources

How can designers prove their competence?

35   An important part of the CDM Regulations deals with the need to employ people and organisations who are aware of their duties and have the competence and resources to see that they comply with the duties the Regulations place upon them. The Approved Code of Practice (ACoP) suggests that the person who engages a designer should make certain enquiries.

How can designers show they have adequate resources?

36   The following list is a summary of the items that could be looked for:

(a) a familiarity with the construction processes;

(b) knowledge of the impact of design on health and safety;

(c) an awareness of health and safety legislation and appropriate risk assessment methods;

(d) suitable practices and procedures to take account of health and safety in design and communicate information to the planning supervisor;

(e) trained staff and/or access to advice;

(f) adequate time and other resources allowed for the work;

(g) support facilities (such as access to current health and safety information); and

(h) a clear method of dealing with design changes and suitable methods of communicating revised information.

General guidance on competence and the allocation of resources is given in Appendix 1.

37   There will inevitably be a learning period, particularly for designers who have not previously been closely involved with construction health and safety. However, with experience of the Regulations in operation, there will be an increase in the levels of competence available and in the evidence available to demonstrate that competence. The level of competence and the actual competence required will depend on the project and the complexity of the health and safety issues involved. The greater the severity and range of health and safety issues and the greater the number of parties involved in the project, the greater the level of competence needed.

Designers should be prepared to provide evidence of their ability to carry out the duties placed on them - clients will ask for this.

The planning supervisor

38   Designers need to understand the function and duties of the planning supervisor. The latter is appointed by the client for all except the smallest projects and work for domestic clients (work on the client's own home). The planning supervisor is a new role in the construction team and is unlike the more familiar roles of consultants and statutory inspectors. The main points to bear in mind are:

(a) the planning supervisor is a statutory appointment. If the appointment is terminated before the end of the construction phase a replacement has to be appointed;

(b) the appointment must be made as soon as the client knows enough about the project to judge who would be suitable to take on the planning supervisor role;

(c) there is nothing in the CDM Regulations to say that the planning supervisor should always be independent of the other parties to the project. The only requirement is that the planning supervisor should be competent and adequately resourced for health and safety. One of the designers (or design practices) involved can be the planning supervisor. Equally contractors or clients themselves can take on the role. Other than for the smallest of projects it is unlikely that the planning supervisor role will be carried out by an individual.

What does the planning supervisor do?

39   The duties of the planning supervisor include seeing that the formal procedures, eg notification to the Health and Safety Executive (HSE) are carried out. The planning supervisor has to ensure that:

(a)   a pre-tender stage health and safety plan and a health and safety file are prepared;

(b)   adequate consideration and information on health and safety is included in the design;

(c)   reasonable steps are taken to allow for co-operation between designers on health and safety matters.

The duties also include being in a position to advise the client on the competence and resources of prospective designers and principal contractors and on the adequacy of the health and safety plan which has to be developed before the construction phase starts.

40   There is nothing in the CDM Regulations to say that the health and safety plans or health and safety file have to be prepared by the planning supervisor. It is simply the planning supervisor's duty to see that they are prepared and available at the appropriate stages in the project. However, the person who actually produces the plans and the file should be decided at an early stage, as should format and broad content (see Appendices 2 and 3).

> *The role of planning supervisor has been made as flexible as possible so that it can be adapted to the many different types of project and contract used in construction.*

The pre-tender stage health and safety plan and the health and safety file

41   The pre-tender stage health and safety plan deals with health and safety issues relevant to the construction phase. The file holds information which becomes relevant when the construction phase, or parts of it, have been completed.

What is the pre-tender stage health and safety plan?

42   The pre-tender stage health and safety plan is continually developed to be ready at the same time as the tender documents. Once the plan is finalised, it goes out with the tender documents to alert tenderers to conditions and hazards associated with the project. For example, it should include relevant information on buried services, hazardous materials, or official guidance applying to particular risks and on operations for which a particular consideration of working methods is required, as well as on site welfare facilities. Details of information which may be contained within a pre-tender stage health and safety plan are given in Appendix 2. If there is no tendering, the plan should be prepared at a similar stage in the development of the design, eg when production drawings and specifications are being finalised. The principal contractor will take the pre-tender stage plan and develop it to suit the organisation and working practices of the contractor's organisation for managing the construction phase of the project.

What is the health and safety file?

43   The file may consist of as-built specifications and drawings and can be part of a maintenance manual for the structure. In whatever form it is produced it focuses on health and safety issues such as:

■   procedures and requirements for cleaning and repair of the structure;

■   operation and maintenance of plant and equipment;

■   instructions for equipment;

■   design loadings for structural elements.

44   If potential hazards are built into the structure such as pre-tensioned beams or suspended floors, details should be given. The file should include 'as-built' drawings and may contain the manuals produced by equipment suppliers and specialist contractors. Information for the file will need to be gathered during the design stage of the project. It may be added to and updated while the contractor is on site. The completed file is only required on completion of the project. At that point the planning supervisor has to ensure that the final version of the health and safety file is handed to the client for future reference.

45   Although it is the planning supervisor's duty to ensure the pre-tender stage health and safety plan and the file are produced and are available at the right times, designers will inevitably be called on to provide much of the information that provides the basic structure for the two documents. In many cases designers are likely to be asked to prepare at least parts of both the plan and the file. From the early stages of the project and while the design is being developed or reviewed, relevant information should be gathered together for eventual use in these documents. Further details of health and safety files can be found in Appendix 3 and in the ACoP.

Duties under the Regulations

46   For a full description of the duties that the CDM Regulations place on those involved in a project, it is essential to consult the CDM Regulations themselves and the ACoP. Table 4 on page 18 summarises the duties and shows how they apply to different types and sizes of project. Designers should note that while the Regulations do not generally apply to very small jobs they do apply to all demolition jobs. Domestic clients (those having work done on their own homes) are exempted from the Regulations. When work is done for a domestic client, neither a planning supervisor nor a principal contractor need be appointed.

47   Designers working for domestic clients still have a duty to consider health and safety while designing and to include relevant health and safety information within the design. They will not enjoy the assistance of a planning supervisor to co-ordinate health and safety issues. When working for domestic clients, designers should particularly ensure that the design documents which will be provided to the contractor include all necessary health and safety information.

Ensure that the application of the Regulations to the project has been fully considered before assuming they do not apply.

Table 4 Summary of duties under the CDM Regulations and their application to projects

TYPE OF CONSTRUCTION PROJECT *(except those for which a local authority is the enforcing authority)	Duty holders				
	CLIENT/CLIENT'S AGENT OR DEVELOPER	DESIGNERS	PLANNING SUPERVISOR	PRINCIPAL CONTRACTOR	OTHER CONTRACTORS
(i) Work (including demolition) done for domestic clients (ie, work done on a home owner's dwelling).	No duty unless work done by a developer.	Duty to: apply hierarchy of risk control; avoid foreseeable risks, to combat risks at source and to give priority to protection of all, before protection of the individual; include adequate information in the design. No duty to co-operate with planning supervisor (as there need not be one).	No planning supervisor needs to be appointed	No principal contractor needs to be appointed	No CDM duties except: notification duties for contractors on larger projects.
(ii) Any project which is not notifiable and which involves four or less people on site	No duty.	Duties as above.	No planning supervisor needs to be appointed	No principal contractor needs to be appointed	No CDM duty.

Project	Client Duty to:	Designers Duty to:	Planning supervisor Duty to:	Principal contractor Duty to:	Contractors Duty to:
(iii) Any project lasting not longer than 30 days (but five people or more working at a time).	appoint planning supervisor and principal contractor;	make clients aware of duties placed upon them by the CDM Regulations before beginning design work;	ensure that HSE is notified of project;	ensure construction phase H&S plan sets out arrangements for health and safety and includes information on welfare;	co-operate with principal contractor;
(iv) Any project involving 500 or less person days, construction work (but five people or more working at a time).	make reasonable enquiries to assess the competence and proposed resources for health and safety of all those appointed or for whom or with whom all arrangements are made for work to be done;	apply the hierarchy risk of control; avoid foreseeable risks, combat risks at source and give priority to protection of all, before protection of the individual;	see that design includes adequate information and consideration of risks;	take steps to ensure co-operation between all contractors;	provide principal contractor with information affecting H&S, or would be relevant to the H&S file;
(v) Any project lasting longer than 30 days or involving more than 500 person days.	ensure required H&S information is available to the planning supervisor;	include adequate H&S information in the design;	ensure co-operation between designers;	ensure every contractor and employee complies with any construction phase H&S rules in the plan;	comply with principal contractor's directions;
(vi) Any project involving demolition or dismantling (except in private houses).	ensure construction phase H&S plan is adequate before work starts on site;	co-operate with planning supervisor and other designers.	advise client and contractors on competence and resourcing;	ensure only authorised people are allowed on site;	comply with rules in H&S plan;
	ensure H&S file is available.		ensure a pre-tender stage H&S plan is prepared;	ensure notification is displayed;	obtain relevant health and safety information from the principal contractor before starting work on the site.
			ensure a H&S file is prepared and delivered to the client on completion.	provide the planning supervisor with information;	
				ensure every contractor has required information and training;	
				ensure that there is opportunity for H&S discussion with employees and the self-employed working on the project.	

† H&S = health and safety

*Projects where the local authority is the health and safety enforcing authority, (eg minor works in offices, shops and warehouses) which are not otherwise notifiable, so CDM does not apply

2

The practical steps that designers can take

48   The Regulations define duties for designers. The ACoP recognises that the CDM Regulations will require a radical change in culture for many of the new duty holders. Designers themselves have to find the practical steps that can translate the duties into actions. Some of the work that can be done to bring about such a change is described in this section.

Weighing issues simultaneously

49   **Health and safety should not be an afterthought.** This may be better understood by civil engineers than by designers of buildings because many civil engineering projects involve obvious and clearly defined risks. When designing a bridge to be built over a busy road the safety aspects of the operation have to be considered from the outset. There may be several ways of tackling the work. The engineers can be expected to consider the safety of each approach together with the costs, speed of construction and the durability and appearance of the finished work. Building designers should learn to work in a similar way when choosing between design options.

50   Health and safety should be given due weight. When a design is developed the requirements of health and safety can be included with the other requirements. Designers should at the very least learn to identify the major risks. When the pros and cons of different specifications are being considered health and safety should figure in the balance of possibilities. Throughout the specific work and alongside the many requirements that shape the building, civil engineering or engineering construction work, attention should be paid to the health and safety and related information requirements of those who will construct, maintain and eventually dismantle the structure at the end of its life.

51   There is no easy answer to deciding the importance that should be given to health and safety. Perhaps the best way to look at the relative weightings that could be given is to examine the consequences that will result from a choice or decision. In the end a professional judgement has to be made - it should be a decision that involves a proper exercise of judgement which takes account of health and safety issues.

Designers should tackle health and safety and other design requirements simultaneously.

Anticipating hazards and risks

52   Designers may believe that other professionals have more experience of critical health and safety issues, or that contractors or other professionals are in a better position to ensure the procedures adopted are as safe as they can be. However, if, unlike designers, others are not involved at the start, when they do participate it may be too late to avoid a hazard that need never have existed.

53   It is often the case that a design decision establishes the hazard that has to be faced and the contractor is then left to manage the risk. For example, a contractor can be faced with a design in which the only possible site access is in a dangerous position, simply because the designer has not foreseen the need to provide enough

space for vehicles to pull in off the road. Had the problem been appreciated at the design stage it might easily have been avoided, but the construction phase of a project is too late to make a major change in layout. All the contractor can do is find ways of managing the problem, eg to employ a banksman to organise safer vehicle movement.

At what stage should designers start to consider health and safety?

54   The most important contribution a designer can make to improve health and safety often has to be made at the start of a project. Opportunities can be lost if health and safety is not considered at this early stage. Rather than looking on health and safety as a matter that can be postponed until other issues are out of the way, designers should deliberately bring consideration forward to ensure that the other issues are resolved in a way that eliminates risk so far as reasonably practicable.

> *Designers should try to foresee hazards and should bring forward consideration of health and safety issues.*

Ensuring that health and safety is included in the brief

55   The Regulations require designers to make clients aware of the duties imposed on them. If the Regulations apply, the client is required to make certain critical decisions about the formal appointment of the planning supervisor and the principal contractor. The client has to be satisfied that there is a health and safety plan that complies with the Regulations before allowing construction work to start. There will also be times when the client's acceptance or rejection of a design scheme, budget or programme will have health and safety implications. However, nothing in the Regulations suggests that all clients are expected to have an expertise in health and safety. Many clients will have little knowledge of construction matters in general and still less of health and safety. They are, in fact, expected to take advice. When designers first discuss projects with clients, they make them aware of the CDM Regulations and their implications for the project. Designers should not start work until they have taken reasonable steps to make their clients aware of the duties placed upon clients by the Regulations.

56   Clients should be told that:

(a)   they need to appoint a planning supervisor and principal contractor;

(b)   before making arrangements for designers or contractors to do work under the CDM Regulations they should be reasonably satisfied that those they appoint or make arrangements with to carry out work are both competent and have allocated, or will allocate, adequate resources to enable them to perform their functions under the Regulations;

(c)   they should ensure that the planning supervisor is provided with relevant health and safety information about the project which is in their possession, or could be obtained by making reasonable enquiries;

(d)   they should see that construction work does not start until the principal contractor has prepared a suitable health and safety plan;

(e)   the health and safety file should be kept available for inspection.

57 Designers can also assist clients by:

(a) making clear who is able to advise the client on different a and safety and what information they are expected to provide;

(b) identifying acceptable procedures and solutions to problems likely to be met and noting the associated costs;

(c) setting down the arrangements for maintenance; and

(d) informing them that they may appoint an agent to act as client for the purposes of the Regulations (further details about the client's agent can be found in the ACoP).

Designers should alert clients to the health and safety duties placed on them as clients when the project brief is defined. These issues are addressed in the health and safety plan which the planning supervisor should ensure is produced.

Assessing risk

58 The appropriate level of risk assessment will vary from project to project and from one operation to another. Where it is clear that there are serious hazards, a thorough study of the risks and a detailed method statement may be needed, eg when glazing is to be replaced over an active shopping mall or when explosives are to be used to open a channel through rock. The assessment may involve a detailed analysis but more often all that is appropriate is a simple judgement based on the seriousness of any incident that could result and the degree of exposure to the hazard. In a project that does not involve exceptionally hazardous operations, design reviews at key stages (eg before tender documents and working drawings are started) should help to identify hazards needing investigation. Sometimes it may be possible to avoid a hazard altogether but in many cases, where alternative methods of construction are possible, it will be necessary to assess the risks within each alternative so that safety measures can be considered and the health and safety aspects of alternatives can be taken into account.

When necessary, designers should be prepared to make an assessment of risks.

Using information available

59 There is a great deal of information in existence on construction health and safety. Although rarely written specifically for designers, much of it can be used by them when carrying out their duties under the CDM Regulations. Also of relevance is the health and safety legislation governing:

(a) materials (such as lead, asbestos and other hazardous substances);

(b) activities (such as demolition or removal of contaminated soil);

(c) welfare requirements (including sanitary accommodation and first aid);

(d) environmental conditions (resulting from noise and dust);

(e) health and safety policies (which are required in written form for all but the smallest firms and which will be operated in existing buildings and in completed buildings).

60   There is other information in the form of authoritative guidance, accident statistics and reports and standard procedures. Some sources of information are listed at the back of this publication. The list includes information specially prepared as guidance for designers carrying out their CDM duties. For further information on hazards in construction work, please see Section 5. However, knowing of a publication, or even having it to hand, does not ensure that it is used. Designers should make sure that design reviews and risk assessments include consideration of the relevant information.

Designers should make full use of the information that is available.

61   The individual expertise and experience of any one designer is inevitably limited. It is important, therefore, that designers recognise the limits of their knowledge and stop to seek advice rather than continuing on the basis of poorly founded assumptions. Knowing when to seek expert advice on health and safety is a skill designers need to develop. Over time, designers will build up networks of those who can provide such advice as they have in other areas.

Designers need to recognise when special health and safety measures and advice are needed.

Using reference publications and relevant experience

62   Designers' duties include informing clients of their CDM duties and co-operation with the planning supervisor and with other designers. There will also be other opportunities for designers to discuss and develop their knowledge of health and safety and see how their design has an impact on the construction process. Colleagues, designers working on similar projects, HSE and the professional institutions, may be able to offer suggestions and advice from experience on other projects. More specific advice is often available from the manufacturers and suppliers of products and from specialist firms who have had responsibility for the safety of a particular operation on a number of sites.

63   The principal contractor has responsibility for managing health and safety on site (contractors have had this responsibility for many years). Their know-how should not be overlooked. Competitive tendering can make it difficult to consult with the principal contractor at an early stage in the project, but if tendering procedures allow, early consultation should be sought because there will be a better opportunity to put into practice health and safety measures that the contractor knows and has used.

Designers can consult with others who have health and safety responsibilities.

Section 4

How different types of construction work will be affected

64 The application of the CDM Regulations is intended to be flexible. They have to work for different types of project and with different contractual arrangements. The examples given here show how the Regulations can be applied to a variety of projects and, in consequence, how the input of designers and the other duty holders will vary. It is not intended to deal with the technical aspects of the work described.

Traditional building - selective competitive tendering

> **EXAMPLE**
>
> The client, who has not previously commissioned a building, appoints an architect who explains the client's responsibilities under the CDM Regulations. The architect is not prepared to act as planning supervisor but recommends a structural engineering practice that has the competence and resources to take on this role. The engineer and architect work together to produce the pre-tender stage health and safety plan and to collect information which can be included in the health and safety file with input from the quantity surveyor, the design department of a nominated services contractor and the specialist firm designing the temporary support to a large cantilevered loading canopy (the construction phase health and safety plan details the precautions to be taken when striking this temporary work). The tender list is drawn up after a pre-selection process has eliminated contractors with insufficient competence or resources to act as the principal contractor.

Series of similar buildings - design and build contract

> **EXAMPLE**
>
> The client's in-house architect has developed a general brief, which includes the client's policy towards health and safety and some specific design requirements for health and safety that apply to all the buildings in the series (eg for boundary fencing, use of materials and access to plant). The bids by design and build contractors are required to include evidence of competence and resources for their design department and the sections of the firm that will take on the roles of planning supervisor and principal contractor. The successful design and build tenderer prepares the health and safety plan and file internally and must arrange for co-operation and exchange of information between the departments involved.

4

Housing site development - separate contracts to build houses on freehold sites

E X A M P L E

The client is a developer and contractor. The architect, who is also appointed as planning supervisor, has negotiated planning permission to develop a site for several large detached houses. The client sells each plot of land together with a contract to build a house on it. The architect draws up a pre-tender stage health and safety plan and later a file for each house with an input from the client who appoints his own firm as the principal contractor (the firm has adequate competence and resources to implement the CDM Regulations).

Building a private house - contract with a domestic client

E X A M P L E

The purchaser of one of the sites referred to in the last example wishes to change the design of the house and negotiates to buy a plot without the commitment to have the house built by the developer. A building surveyor negotiates planning permission for a different design. As the project is now for a domestic client the full scope of the CDM Regulations does not apply and there is no formal requirement to appoint a planning supervisor or a principal contractor, or to prepare a health and safety plan or file. However, the building surveyor's duty as a designer, and that of other designers involved, to avoid or control the foreseeable risks and to provide information still remains.

Road and bridge - civil engineering contract

E X A M P L E

The client is a local authority with a rolling programme of highway works. A civil engineering practice is employed as planning supervisor for all the client's highway works. A different civil engineering practice is employed as consultant for site investigation and design of a new road bridge. Alternative designs are developed which include outline method statements and a report on the risk assessments which have been carried out. These are prepared in association with the engineers acting as the planning supervisor.

One design approach is selected and developed to tender documentation stage together with a pre-tender stage health and safety plan and a preliminary version of the health and safety file. The gas, electricity and water companies contribute to both the plan and the file. The client obtains competitive tenders for the work. The tender conditions require that the principal contractor appointed has an established and compatible health and safety policy. The original design practice is re-employed to supervise the work and, in co-operation with the planning supervisor, changes in the design and method of construction suggested by the principal contractor are agreed as more information about site conditions becomes available.

Other variations are agreed as more information about new equipment also becomes available. The principal contractor amends the construction phase health and safety plan as the variations are authorised. The final version of the health and safety file is brought up to date to include the variations before it is handed to the client on completion.

New office building - fitting out contract

E X A M P L E

The client has leased two floors of a new office building 'shell'. An interior designer is going to prepare a fitting out scheme. The designers, planning supervisor and principal contractor of the shell are no longer involved. The client for the shell (now the building freeholder) passes the health and safety file (from the shell contract) via the lessor to the interior designer, who is able to show evidence of the competence and resources necessary to act as planning supervisor and to produce a pre-tender stage health and safety plan for the fitting out work. To save time, a principal contractor who has already been pre-qualified for health and safety purposes, is appointed under a negotiated contract. The interior designer works with the principal contractor to develop a health and safety plan for the construction phase. When it is ready the client is advised that the work can start. Once the work is complete the interior designer prepares an additional section for the health and safety file relating to the fitting out work and presents it to the client.

4

Programmed maintenance
- term contract for painting

E X A M P L E

The client is a firm that occupies several commercial buildings. The firm's facilities manager has previous experience in the construction industry and sufficient knowledge of design to prepare routine maintenance contracts. A contractor is employed on a two year term contract for exterior painting and window repair. The full scope of the CDM Regulations will not apply to the painting work on most of the firm's buildings as only three workers will be employed and each building will take less than a month to paint. However, the Regulations will apply to the painting and repair work on the headquarters' building as it is expected to take two months.

The facilities manager, who is the firm's health and safety officer, discharges the duties of the planning supervisor for the work to the headquarters building on behalf of his employers who appoint themselves as planning supervisor. The facilities manager draws up a pre-tender stage health and safety plan. In consultation with the facilities manager, the painting contractor who is appointed as principal contractor for the project, draws up a construction phase health and safety plan and also a health and safety file as the work is carried out. The file adds information to the building's records, eg recording that some cradle fixings had corroded and that temporary cradle brackets should be used in those locations.

Supply and installation of
new plant - engineering
procurement and
construction management
(EPCM) contract

E X A M P L E

The client is a manufacturer who wishes to replace an obsolete production unit. He places an EPCM contract with the specialist engineering contractor to design, procure, supervise the installation and commission the new plant for the production unit. As the installation of the plant could involve a person falling more than 2 metres, the CDM Regulations will apply (regulation 2, definition of structure). The engineering contractor is appointed as both planning supervisor and principal contractor.

Acting as planning supervisor the contractor initiates a health and safety plan for the proposed work and assesses and co-ordinates the design activities of the suppliers of the specialised packages of the plant. This ensures compatibility with the rest of the plant design from a health and safety point of view. The planning supervisor also begins to compile the health and safety file. As the installation contract ends with mechanical completion, the construction phase health and safety plan has to set out the roles and responsibilities of the client and the engineering contractor for the pre-commissioning and commissioning phases and include all design information relevant to their safe completion.

The health and safety file is handed to the client on completion of commissioning, having been updated during the installation and commissioning phases by the engineering contractor acting as planning supervisor.

4

Hazards and risks in construction work

65   Tables 1, 2 and 3 on pages 4 to 6 give information on causes of death, injury and ill health in construction. Designers cannot eliminate all health and safety risks, but they can make a significant contribution. Also, by tackling risks at source, giving priority to measures which give protection to everyone affected by the risk, and passing on health and safety information, they can assist the contractor who must manage the remaining risks effectively.

Hazard and risk

Hazard - the potential to cause harm.

Risk - the likelihood that harm will occur.

Identification of hazards

66   A design feature may have none, one, or a combination of hazards associated with it, and tables 1, 2, and 3 show many of the matters of greatest concern. At an early stage in the design process, the designer will need to consider general hazards, such as falls. As the design detail develops, hazards relating to specific items will need to be considered. The tables, together with the principles illustrated in the examples on pages 34 to 40 can be used at an early stage in the design process to point out where in the construction and maintenance stages the hazards are likely to occur, eg general hazards such as:

Falls from heights	**Harmful substances**	**Manual handling**
Structural erection	Contaminated land	Building blocks
Window cleaning	Paint application	Long roof sheets
Cladding	Stone cutting	Sharp brick ties
Roof work		

The information could also be applied to particular design features, eg:

Flat roof
Falls from height
Harmful substances (sealing compound)
Fragile roof lights

Carrying out risk assessment

67   The purpose of risk assessment in this case is to indicate to designers the potential effect of their design on the health and safety of workers. As a consequence, designers will be able to judge the weight they should give to health and safety and whether, on balance, the design can be left unchanged or should be altered to reduce the health and safety risk. What is 'reasonably practicable' (which also involves cost and other design goals) becomes part of this judgement.

68   A precise estimate of risk is not required; it would be too time consuming in practice and, in any case, lack of data often makes it impossible. There is a variety of risk assessment methods, ranging from the crudely qualitative to the relatively sophisticated quantitative. Any method chosen will, to some degree, be subjective and arbitrary but, nevertheless, can prove useful provided it is appropriate for its purpose and its limitations are recognised.

69 At its simplest, the risk arising from a hazard depends on two elements:

(a) the **likely severity of harm** caused if the hazard manifests itself in an accident or ill health (consequence);

(b) the **likelihood that harm will occur** (frequency).

The contribution of the separate elements needs to be decided first, then risk is assessed from the combination of these two elements.

Likely severity of harm

70 If three categories of severity are assumed, the table that follows, which is based on the experience of HSE, can be taken as a guide to the likely severity of the harm caused by the hazard.

'HIGH' - Fatality; major injury or illness causing long-term disability.
'MEDIUM' - Injury or illness causing short-term disability.
'LOW' - Other injury or illness.

	HIGH	MEDIUM	LOW	
Falls from height	■			more than 2 metres
		■		2 metres or less
Being struck by mobile plant	■			
Tripping			■	
Collapse	■			
Manual handling		■	■	depending on the object handled
Moving objects	■			
Electricity	■			normal voltage and above
			■	110v and below
Contact with moving machinery	■			
Fire	■			
Harmful substances	■	■	■	depending on the substance concerned
Noise and vibration	■	■	■	depending on exposure levels

Likelihood that harm will occur

71   Since the primary concern for the designer is what they can do to eliminate hazards to reduce risk, the measures which contractors can take on their own behalf to protect their workers (eg temporary edge protection, personal protective equipment) should be discounted by the designer at this stage. Even though contractors could control risks which particular hazards give rise to by the application of well known precautions, the designer must still give consideration to how hazards can be eliminated and risks reduced.

72   Designers will have to analyse the likely method(s) of construction and/or maintenance etc to be able to make a judgement as to likelihood that harm will occur. Designers need to consider whether hazard and worker will coincide; how many workers, how often, for how long. Again, only a crude, qualitative judgement can, and need, be made, for example, as follows:

'**HIGH**' - Certain or near certain to occur.
'**MEDIUM**' - Reasonably likely to occur.
'**LOW**' - Very seldom or never occurs.

Assessing both severity and likelihood

73   Take the hazard 'falls from height' from the unprotected edge of a 3 metre high roof onto which access will be needed to carry out maintenance work. The severity element is 'high'. If the maintenance involves one worker going onto the roof once every five years the likelihood element might be judged 'low'; one worker once a month, 'medium'; ten workers once a day, 'high'.

74   Take the hazard 'being struck by mobile plant' on a construction site. The severity element is 'high'. The likelihood element depends on the amount of plant, and the size and layout of the site, so on a house building site it would probably be 'low' to 'medium'; on a civil engineering site involving earth moving, 'medium' to 'high'; on carriageway repairs, 'high'.

75   Take the use of 'hazardous substances' in painting. The severity hazard associated with a water-based paint is probably 'low', with an isocyanate paint, 'high'. The likelihood element with brush application is 'low' to 'medium'; with spray application, 'high'.

76   The product of the elements will give some measure of the assessed risk which, in turn, can be seen as exerting a pressure on designers to alter the design. Clearly, a 'high' x 'high' risk exerts a very high degree of pressure, 'low' x 'low' virtually none. Designers may conclude that design alteration is not practicable, but they should be prepared to justify their choice in the light of the particular risk assessment.

Reduction of risk through design and specification

77   The following examples show the ways in which designers can design and specify to reduce the risk from the hazards identified. They are not intended to be comprehensive; instead they look at some likely areas of intervention.

78   When designing to reduce risk, designers should apply the principles of protection. The best approach is to prevent the hazard arising and so avoid the risk. If this is not reasonably practicable the risk should be combated at source. Priority should be given to measures to control the risk that will provide communal protection. Measures to control risk by means of personal protection should only be assumed as a last resort.

Site and site layout

79   This section provides some examples of options available to designers to eliminate hazards and control risks. Where risks cannot be eliminated through design, additional information may be required within the pre-tender health and safety plan. This will help contractors tendering to explain how they will manage the risks.

Hazard 1: Struck by mobile plant

Principle of protection	Examples of application
COMBAT AT SOURCE	Design the site (eg the location of structures on the site, positioning site entrances and exits, and travel routes) to: 1 provide drivers entering, moving around and leaving the site with good visibility by avoiding blind corners etc);
COMMUNAL PROTECTION	2 allow a one-way system to be adopted for delivery, and for spoil removal vehicles; 3 segregate pedestrians from transport.

Hazard 2: Electricity

Principle of protection	Examples of application
AVOID	Design the layout (ie the location of structures) to avoid work and mobile plant movement taking place in the vicinity of overhead electric cables. Alternatively, arrange for the lines to be relocated to a safe area.

Groundwork   *Hazard 1: Collapse*

Principle of protection	Examples of application
AVOID/COMBAT AT SOURCE	Consider the effect of proposed excavations on the stability of adjacent, existing structures.
COMMUNAL PROTECTION	If temporary instability cannot be avoided, include principles of temporary support in the design.

Hazard 2: Hazardous substances

Principle of protection	Examples of application
AVOID	Locate structures, pipe runs etc to avoid contaminated areas of the site.

Hazard 3: Noise and vibration

Principle of protection	Examples of application
AVOID	Use quieter methods of construction such as bored piling rather than hammer driven.

Erecting structures

Hazard 1: Falls from height

Principle of protection	Examples of application
AVOID	Avoid/reduce the need for workers making connections at height by designing structures which can be connected at ground level and lifted into position by crane.
COMMUNAL PROTECTION	Erection of stairways and floors as the frame is erected can provide safe access to heights and safe working places at height. Structural designs should allow for the incorporation of guard rails or similar edge protection.
PERSONAL PROTECTION	As an example, steelwork should be designed to take safety harnesses, manlocks and running lines where necessary.

Hazard 2: Collapse

Principle of protection	Examples of application
AVOID/COMBAT AT SOURCE	Avoid designs which involve temporary instability during erection, or specify an erection sequence which avoids it. Provide sufficient information to enable contractors to develop a safe erection sequence and/or co-operate and share relevant information with the contractor via the planning supervisor.
COMMUNAL PROTECTION	If temporary instability cannot be avoided, include details of temporary support in the design.

Hazard 3: Fire

Principle of protection	Examples of application
COMMUNAL PROTECTION	Erect stairways early in the construction process to provide means of escape in case of fire.

Cladding and brickwork

Hazard 1: Falls from height

Principle of protection	Examples of application
COMBAT AT SOURCE	Cladding panels can be designed to reduce the risk of panels falling on to the worker fixing it in position. Do not specify very long roof panels which are very awkward to handle, particularly in windy conditions.

Hazard 2: Fire

Principle of protection	Examples of application
COMBAT AT SOURCE	Minimise the fire loading arising from the materials and products stored and used in a structure under construction by specifying non/low flammable or combustible materials and products.

Hazard 3: Noise and vibration

Principle of protection	Examples of application
AVOID/COMBAT AT SOURCE	Avoid specifying finishes which involve noisy operations such as concrete scabbling.
COMBAT AT SOURCE	Where possible reduce the need for concrete or steel cutting by making proper allowance for tolerances, ie not relying on perfect fit nor on cutting away to make things fit. Leave gaps and specify expanding grout, mastic or resilient materials such as joint fillers. Reduce the need for abrading, eg by designing to facilitate larger concrete pours, so reducing the need for scabbling.

Hazard 4: Falling objects

Principle of protection	Examples of application
COMBAT AT SOURCE/ COMMUNAL PROTECTION	Ensure the design details of items to be lifted include attachment points which will support the load.

Hazard 5: Manual handling

Principle of protection	Examples of application
AVOID/COMBAT AT SOURCE	Avoid specifying heavy building blocks, to prevent back injury. Ensure the design details of heavy items include attachment points for lifting gear.

Installation and maintenance of services

Hazard 1: Falls from heights

Principle of protection	Examples of application
AVOID	Specify light fittings which can be lowered or manoeuvred to floor or landing level for lamp or tube changing.

Hazard 2: Tripping

Principle of protection	Examples of application
AVOID	Avoid low-level pipe runs in plant rooms.

Hazard 3: Manual handling

Principle of protection	Examples of application
COMBAT AT SOURCE	Plant room entrances should be designed (shape, size, access not via ladders) and plant rooms laid out to allow safe handling of plant and equipment.
COMBAT AT SOURCE	Equip plant rooms with lifting beams where heavy plant might have to be handled.

Hazard 4: Electricity

Principle of protection	Examples of application
COMBAT AT SOURCE	Equipment providing mechanical and electrical services to the structure should include means of isolation from the electrical supply which is easily understood, ie laid out in the same sequence as the plant and clearly labelled.

Finishes   *Hazard 1: Hazardous substances*

Principle of protection	Examples of application
AVOID	Avoid using the substance at all. For example, specify a natural substance finish rather than paint.
	Substitute with a safer substance. For example, specify water-based paints, glues etc which are generally safer than solvent-based ones.
	Specify off-site production (where conditions are more easily controlled), eg factory decoration of components.
	Avoid dust-producing processes. For example, avoid chasing by designing to provide ducts and conduits, routeing pipes and wires through voids rather than wall thicknesses and using surface fixed conduit.
	Specify off-site finishing and polishing of cladding etc.
	Do not specify hazardous substances for use in confined or difficult to ventilate areas.
COMBAT AT SOURCE	Specify substances and application methods which minimise atmospheric contamination. For example, paints which can be brushed rather than sprayed; fire protection board or sheet which can be fixed to steelwork, rather than firespray.
	Reduce the need for dust-producing cutting by making proper allowance for tolerances, ie not relying on perfect fit nor on cutting away to make things fit.

Refurbishment and repair

Hazard 1: Struck by mobile plant

Principle of protection	Examples of application
COMBAT AT SOURCE	Locate features such as road bridge piers in a position where workers carrying out repair on them are not brought in close proximity to traffic.

Hazard 2: Collapse

Principle of protection	Examples of application
COMBAT AT SOURCE	Specify a sequence of removal and replacement of structural members to maintain stability during refurbishment.

Hazard 3: Fire

Principle of protection	Examples of application
COMBAT AT SOURCE	Minimise the fire loading arising from the materials and products stored and used in a structure under refurbishment by specifying non/low flammable or combustible materials and products. Provide storage for flammable materials off site in a less vulnerable environment.
COMMUNAL PROTECTION	Sequence refurbishment to maintain existing means of escape.

Roof work maintenance

Hazard 1: Falls from height

Principle of protection	Examples of application
AVOID	Do not place features at height on the roof, eg plant rooms, which require frequent access for maintenance. Do not specify fragile roofing material through which workers can fall.
COMMUNAL PROTECTION	Incorporate permanent walkways, platforms, travelling gantries across fragile roofs. Install permanent edge protection such as guard rails, parapet walls on flat roofs.

Glass cleaning and
maintenance

Hazard 1: Falls from height

Principle of protection	Examples of application
AVOID	Specify reversible windows which can be fully cleaned on both sides from within the building.
COMMUNAL PROTECTION	Incorporate permanent walkways, platforms, travelling gantries at high/ceiling level, to clean atria, windows and skylights (internal and external).
PERSONAL PROTECTION	Provide anchors for safety lines where no other protection is available for window cleaning.

Renovation

Hazard 1: Health hazards from substances

Principle of protection	Examples of application
AVOID	Avoid using the substances at all. For example, specify replacement of rotten timber rather than remedial treatment with pesticides.
AVOID/COMBAT AT SOURCE	Reduce exposure by designing for reduced frequency of maintenance such as low maintenance materials, facade features to minimise the effects of weathering etc. Do not specify hazardous substances for use in confined areas.
COMMUNAL PROTECTION	Maximise the ventilation (mechanically if necessary) of confined areas where hazardous substances have to be used, or can be expected to occur.

Competence and provision for health and safety

1   CDM regulations 8 and 9 contain legal requirements on competence and provision for health and safety. Duties are placed on:

■   the client when appointing a planning supervisor;

■   any person when arranging for a designer to prepare a design or a contractor to carry out or manage construction work.

Under the CDM Regulations a person is a corporate entity or individual, who carries out any of the duties under the Regulations. A client arranging for a designer or a contractor to carry out work, or a designer arranging for another designer to carry out design work has duties to assess health and safety, competency and resourcing. Designers will need to demonstrate their competence to clients.

Competence and provision for health and safety

2   Competence has to be considered in the light of the health and safety duties which will fall to the prospective duty holder. This does not only cover the general issues of the duty holder's organisation and arrangements for managing health and safety. It should also be related to the specific aspects of the project under consideration and the range of differently skilled individuals working within the organisation whose experience can be brought to bear on the project. Competence is not merely a matter of technical qualifications or training achievements, although these may be important. It is a wider assessment of abilities relevant to the work to be carried out.

3   Provision for health and safety means the allocation of adequate resources for the purposes of carrying out duties under the CDM Regulations and complying with health and safety legislation. Resources include people with the appropriate training and skills to carry out the required duties, equipment, technical facilities, and sufficient time to carry out legal duties. Where appropriate, knowledge of health and safety in the following areas of work should be considered:

■   planning and design;

■   preparation of health and safety plans;

■   selection of designers and contractors;

■   sequencing and scheduling of the work;

■   carrying out the construction work or parts of it; and

■   preparation of the health and safety file.

4   The specialist competencies needed within the project can only be determined within that project, but a set of questions will be needed which relates to these special details. There may also be a need to include questions about key people

who are allocated to the project in terms of their experience and knowledge of the particular health and safety issues and their level of awareness and training.

Assessment of
competence and provision
for health and safety

5   The actual assessment process may be quite detailed on large or complex projects, but it can be a very simple one on small works, or those involving low risks. The level of questioning and detail required will depend upon the risks involved in the work and the nature of the construction project. The assessment of competence is crucial to selection and appointment; but it does need to be proportionate and appropriate. The process needs to seek clear answers to well structured questions. It may require additional documentary proof, but there is little point in merely collecting documents; they should fulfil a clear purpose in the assessment process.

6   As part of pre-qualification procedures over the past few years, certain supporting documents have regularly been required during the selection process. However, before asking for any documentation you need to ask yourself what questions you hope it will answer, and have a clear method for assessing the contents. When looking at documents which show historic trends and performance, for example accident information and enforcement records, you need to be aware that this can paint a distorted picture, and may not be a good indicator of current competence. Analysis of documentation may itself need specialist help and advice.

7   The list below outlines some of the more common documents which you could ask for:

- company health and safety documents (including how health and safety considerations are integrated into the design process and risk assessment procedures);

- records of previous enforcement action;

- training records (including relevant continuing professional development);

- quality assurance procedures;

- project review and monitoring documents.

The fact that an organisation cannot provide some or even all of these documents may not mean they are lacking competence or suitable resources. However, you will have to look in some detail to establish why they cannot. On the other hand, avoid being swayed by just lengthy or glossy brochures; there is no guarantee the organisation follows the procedures or even that it wrote the documents.

8   How far this process is followed on smaller contracts is a matter for individual duty holders. It may be that the types of questions and supporting documentary evidence can be compressed into a few minutes' discussion for a small piece of work. However, some competency assessment does need to be done and seen to be carried out.

9   Pre-qualification and selection are already established procedures within the industry. In many cases this is carried out as a two-stage process. The first stage (pre-qualification) is carried out in general terms, sufficient to judge whether an

organisation should be included on the list of those invited to tender for a specific project or to be listed on an approved tender list. The second stage involves organisations who were selected during the first stage, going through a more rigorous second assessment based on their submissions to tender documentation.

10   When carrying out pre-qualification procedures the industry already uses question schedules. These may be tied into consideration of supporting documents or may stand alone. However, some form of assessment is carried out. In paragraphs 11 to 15 in this appendix, a number of key areas have been outlined with some useful questions to ask. This is not meant as an exhaustive list, but it should help duty holders, particularly those undertaking competency assessment for the first time.

Some of the key areas to probe

11   In the following sets of questions, some of the more common areas to consider are outlined. Not every project will need all the areas to be covered. Also, not every duty holder will be able to answer all the questions. However they do provide a basis for assessment. If prospective duty holders can answer all these areas well then they are likely to be able to demonstrate a better performance. Understanding the answers will not be easy in every case, and as with documentation assessment you may need to seek specialist help. Although the questions have been written as if the person answering is an organisation, the same approach can be applied to a professional acting in their own right.

General policy

12   These areas are about the way the duty holder sets out their policy for health and safety:

- How does the organisation demonstrate an understanding of legal duties with respect to health and safety?

- Are there clear processes and procedures within the organisation to carry out risk assessment? How are the results of such assessments turned into effective means of reducing or controlling risk? How are these procedures monitored?

- Is there a clear understanding within the organisation about how accidents and ill health arise in the construction process?

- How does the organisation keep up-to-date with developments in health and safety?

General organisation

13   These questions consider the way the duty holder organises for health and safety matters:

- What arrangements are in place to advise on health and safety matters? Are 'in-house' experts or external consultants relied upon? How is health and safety advice integrated into design procedures?

- How are the capabilities and expertise of individual designers and those of any organisation subcontracted to carry out work assessed?

- Does the organisation arrange health and safety training for its designers?

- How does the organisation ensure that information on health and safety is passed on to designers?

Planning and monitoring

14   This section covers the way design organisations set out their policy for health and safety:

- What procedures does the organisation have for managing information relevant to health and safety? How are changes which are notified to it during the development of a project dealt with?

- How does the organisation monitor performance on health and safety matters? Does it carry out systematic reviews of the impact of their designs on health and safety?

- How does the organisation demonstrate its ability to manage people and processes which will be relevant to health and safety within the project?

Specialist knowledge, abilities, resources and experience

15   In this section questions on special areas which are relevant to specific aspects of the project are asked:

- What specialist back-up and technical facilities does the prospective organisation have which will be relevant to the project?

- What is the organisation's track record on comparable activities?

General points

16   If requested, the planning supervisor should be in a position to give adequate advice to the client on issues of competence and provision for health and safety. This applies when the client arranges for a designer to prepare a design or arranges for a contractor to carry out or manage construction work (CDM regulation 14(c)). Clients with a limited knowledge of the construction process or the issues of competence and provision for health and safety are strongly recommended to take advice from the planning supervisor.

17   Neither the client nor other duty holders need to carry out further checks to ensure that there is a continuing level of competence, nor to check that resources are actually expended in the way that was initially planned. However, if a client or other duty holder chooses to monitor whether resources are being used in the way they were intended to be allocated and a continuing level of competence is being maintained, the health and safety standards tend to be higher than average and significant quality and cost benefits can be achieved.

The pre-tender stage health and safety plan

This appendix helps you to consider the matters which could be included in the pre-tender stage health and safety plan. Some of the items may not be relevant to your project. The level of detail should be determined by the health and safety risks of the project. Projects involving minimal risks call for simple straightforward pre-tender stage health and safety plans. Large projects or those involving significant risks will require more detail.

Possible information for inclusion in the pre-tender stage health and safety plan

1 *Nature of the project*

■ Name of client.

■ Location.

■ Nature of construction work to be carried out.

■ Timescale for completion of the construction work.

2 *The existing environment*

■ Surrounding land uses and related restrictions, eg premises (schools, shops, factories etc) adjacent to proposed construction site, planning restrictions which might affect health and safety.

■ Existing services, eg underground and overhead lines.

■ Existing traffic systems and restrictions, eg access for fire appliances, times of delivery, ease of delivery, parking etc.

■ Existing structures, eg special health problems from materials in existing structures which are being demolished or refurbished, any fragile materials which require special safety precautions, instability problems etc.

■ Ground conditions, eg contamination, gross instability, possible subsidence, old mine workings, underground obstructions etc.

3 *Existing drawings*

■ Available drawings of structure(s) to be demolished or incorporated in the proposed structure(s) (this may include a health and safety file prepared for the structure(s) and held by the client).

4 *The design*

■ Significant hazards or work sequences identified by designers which cannot be avoided or designed out and, where appropriate, a broad indication of the precautions assumed for dealing with them.

■ The principles of the structure's design and any precautions that might be needed or sequences of assembly that need to be followed during construction.

■ Detailed reference to specific problems where contractors will be required to explain their proposals for managing these problems.

5 *Construction materials*

■ Health hazards arising from construction materials where particular precautions are required, either because of their nature or the manner of their intended use. These will have been identified by designers as hazards which cannot be avoided or designed out. They should be specified as far as is necessary to ensure reliable performance by a competent contractor who may be assumed to know the precautionary information that suppliers are, by law, required to provide.

6 *Site-wide elements*

■ Positioning of site access and egress points (eg for deliveries and emergencies).

■ Location of temporary site accommodation.

■ Location of unloading, layout and storage areas.

■ Traffic/pedestrian routes.

7 *Overlap with client's undertaking*

■ Consideration of the health and safety issues which arise when the project is to be located in premises occupied or partly occupied by the client.

8 *Site rules*

■ Specific site rules which the client or the planning supervisor may wish to lay down as a result of points 2 to 7 or for other reasons, eg specific permit-to-work rules, emergency procedures.

9 *Continuing liaison*

■ Procedures for considering the health and safety implications of design elements of the principal contractor's and other contractors' packages.

■ Procedures for dealing with unforeseen eventualities during project execution resulting in substantial design change and which might affect resources.

The health and safety file

1   The health and safety file is a record of information for the end user which focuses on health and safety. The information it contains will alert those who are responsible for the structure and equipment in it of the significant health and safety risks that will need to be dealt with during subsequent use, construction, maintenance and cleaning work.

2   The planning supervisor has to ensure that the health and safety file is prepared. To carry out this task it helps if procedures are set up for obtaining and collating the information to be included in the health and safety file. These procedures may need to detail what information is to be collected, how it is to be collected, presented and stored. They could be part of the planning supervisor's arrangements for dealing with health and safety or part of quality assurance systems. On larger projects it may be necessary to include details relating to the health and safety file in the pre-tender stage health and safety plan to ensure an ordered delivery of information.

Relevant information which could be included in the health and safety file

- 'record' or 'as built' drawings and plans used and produced throughout the construction process;

- the design criteria;

- general details of the construction methods and materials used;

- details of the equipment and maintenance facilities within the structure;

- maintenance procedures and requirements for the structure;

- manuals produced by specialist contractors and suppliers which outline operating and maintenance procedures and schedules for plant and equipment installed as part of the structure; and

- details of the location and nature of utilities and services, including emergency and fire-fighting systems.

3   The planning supervisor may find it useful to discuss the health and safety file with the client. This helps determine what information the client requires and how the client wishes the information to be stored and recorded.

4   Designers and the principal contractor need to ensure so far as is reasonably practicable that any features of the structure which will involve significant risk to health and safety during the structure's lifetime are passed to the planning supervisor. The principal contractor also needs to obtain details of services, plant and equipment which are part of the structure from specialist supply and installation contractors, eg mechanical and electrical contractors and pass this information on.

5   Much of the material for the health and safety file comes from the information which designers are required to provide under CDM regulation 13(2)(b). Providing this information on drawings allows it to be amended if any variations arise during construction. It also allows health and safety information to be stored on the same document (see paragraphs 12 to 16 on page 49).

6   On completion of the project the planning supervisor has to hand over the health and safety file to the client. In some cases it might not be possible for a fully developed health and safety file to be handed over at the end of the project. This may happen because the construction work had to be finished rapidly to meet a tight deadline and completion of the health and safety file was impossible. Clearly a common sense approach may be needed, allowing the health and safety file to be handed over as soon as practical after a completion certificate or similar document has been issued. What is important is that work on producing the file continues throughout the project and is not left until the end.

7   The health and safety file should be kept available for inspection by the client and ideally on the premises to which it relates. It may be useful to store the health and safety file so that it is in two parts. One part will be more relevant for day to day use, eg operational and maintenance manuals. The other part is for longer term use, eg drawings which will only be required when major alteration work is carried out. The health and safety file could, if the client wishes, be stored electronically. It could also be stored on microfiche. In whatever form it is stored, it should be easily accessible.

8   For ease of reference it may be useful for the planning supervisor to produce a document which summarises the key elements of the health and safety file and acts as a quick guide to where the relevant information is stored.

9   When construction work is going to be carried out on a structure for which the client possesses a health and safety file, the client should pass it to the planning supervisor. This forms part of the relevant information which has to be made available. The planning supervisor will then in turn need to ensure that the designers are given the relevant information from the health and safety file. Moreover, relevant parts of the health and safety file may need to be incorporated into the pre-tender stage health and safety plan. Once this construction work has been completed, the health and safety file or parts of it will need to be amended and updated.

10   On a project which involves work on part of a structure for which there is no health and safety file, a health and safety file only has to be created in relation to the construction work carried out and not for the whole of the structure. Eventually, as further work is carried out on that structure, the health and safety file will be added to and amended, allowing an increasingly detailed file to be developed.

11   For projects which involve the building of domestic houses by a developer, each property needs a health and safety file. The infrastructure associated with the development (eg roads and sewers) will also require a health and safety file. Relevant information will need to be passed to the local authority and utility companies.

Drawings   12   The provision of 'as built' and 'as installed' drawings is a common requirement in most contracts. Drawings are a good vehicle for the transmission of information between designer, contractor and back to the client. Drawings can also be a very good way of providing information required under the CDM Regulations, particularly for inclusion in health and safety plans and the health and safety file.

13   The accuracy and usefulness of 'as built' and 'as installed' drawings varies in common experience. While absolute accuracy may not always be possible, attempting to achieve this will improve the provision of information. There can be difficulties in gathering all the information needed for accurate 'as built' and 'as installed' drawings. On large projects it may be necessary to set up clear procedures to collect and validate this data. There may be many ways of presenting and storing this information. This is likely to develop over the coming years.

14   A number of designers and contractors have been developing approaches to 'as built' and 'as installed' drawings and two examples are produced at the back of this publication.

15   In one drawing, some temporary site huts with the mechanical and electrical services all marked are reproduced. This was prepared for a health and safety file as the huts were to be handed to another contractor. A notes section for maintenance and demolition is included.

16   In the other drawing a tender drawing for a cut and cover tunnel has been surrounded by detailed 'as built' information in the drawing margin. Again, there are sections for maintenance and demolition. This was prepared for a health and safety file and is self-explanatory.

3

Glossary

These definitions will help readers to understand the way in which terms are used in this guidance.

Cleaning work: This is the cleaning of any window or any transparent or translucent wall, ceiling or roof in or on a structure, where such cleaning involves a risk of a person falling more than 2 metres.

Client: Clients are those who are involved in a trade, business or other undertaking (whether for profit or not) and for whom construction work is carried out.

Construction work: The carrying out of any building, civil engineering or engineering construction work and includes any of the following:

- the construction, alteration, conversion, fitting out, commissioning, renovation, repair, upkeep, redecoration or other maintenance (including cleaning which involves the use of water or an abrasive at high pressure or the use of substances classified as corrosive or toxic for the purposes of regulation 7 of the Chemicals (Hazard Information and Packaging) Regulations 1993, de-commissioning, demolition or dismantling of a structure;

- the preparation for an intended structure, including site clearance, exploration, investigation (but not site survey) and excavation, and laying or installing the foundations of the structure;

- the assembly of prefabricated elements to form a structure or the disassembly of prefabricated elements which, immediately before such disassembly, formed a structure;

- the removal of a structure or part of a structure or of any product or waste resulting from demolition or dismantling of a structure or from disassembly or prefabricated elements which, immediately before such disassembly, formed a structure; and

- the installation, commissioning, maintenance, repair or removal or mechanical, electrical, gas, compressed air, hydraulic, telecommunications, computer or similar services which are normally fixed within or to a structure;

but does not include the exploration for or extraction of mineral resources or activities preparatory thereto carried out at a place where such exploration or extraction is carried out.

Contractor: Contractors include subcontractors and may also be known as works, specialist trade or nominated contractors. They have health and safety responsibilities for their own employees and others.

Design: Design is a wide term and includes specification and the production of drawings, design details and bills of quantity.

Designers: Designers are the organisations or individuals who carry out the design of the project. Designers may include architects, consulting engineers, quantity surveyors, specifiers, principal contractors and specialist subcontractors.

Hazard: Something with the potential to cause harm.

Health and safety file: This is a record of information for the client which focuses on health and safety. It alerts those who are responsible for the structure and equipment in it of the significant health and safety risks that will need to be dealt with during subsequent use, construction, maintenance, repair and cleaning work.

Health and safety plan: The health and safety plan serves two purposes. The pre-tender stage health and safety plan prepared before the tendering process brings together the health and safety information obtained from the client and designers and aids selection of the principal contractor. The health and safety plan during the construction phase details how the construction work will be managed to ensure health and safety.

Monitoring: Monitoring has two components:

- *active.* This measures performance against plans and standards that have been worked out and agreed at the start of the contract. It shows how much management is committed to achieving objectives and maintaining standards;

- *reactive.* This involves the investigation of accidents and incidents, and the analysis of data from specific investigations.

Notifiable: Construction work is notifiable if it lasts longer than 30 days or will involve more than 500 person days of work.

Planning supervisor: The planning supervisor is a company, partnership, organisation or an individual who co-ordinates and manages the health and safety aspects of design. The planning supervisor also has to ensure that the pre-tender stage of the health and safety plan and the health and safety file are prepared.

Principal contractor: This is the contractor appointed by the client who has the overall responsibility for the management of site operations. This includes the overall co-ordination of site health and safety management.

Project: This means a project which includes or is intended to include construction work.

Risk: The likelihood that harm from a particular hazard will occur and the possible extent of the harm.

Safety method statement: This is a written document laying out the work procedures and sequence of operation to ensure health and safety. It results from the risk assessment carried out for the task or operation and the control measures identified. If the risk is low, a verbal statement may suffice.

So far as reasonably practicable: To carry out a duty 'so far as reasonably practicable' means that the degree of risk in a particular activity can be balanced against the time, trouble, cost and physical difficulty of taking measures to avoid the risk. If these are so disproportionate to the risk that it would be quite unreasonable for the people concerned to have to incur them to prevent it, they are not obliged to do so. The greater the risk, the more likely it is that it is reasonable to go to very substantial expense, trouble and invention to reduce it. However, if the consequences and the extent of a risk are small, insistence on great expense would not be considered reasonable.

Structure: This is:

- any building, steel or reinforced concrete structure (not being a building), railway line or siding, tramway line, dock, harbour, inland navigation, tunnel, shaft, bridge, viaduct, waterworks, reservoir, pipe or pipe-line (whatever, in either case, it contains or is intended to contain), cable, aqueduct, sewer, sewage works, gasholder, road, airfield, sea defence works, river works, drainage works, earthworks, lagoon, dam, wall, caisson, mast, tower, pylon, underground tanks, earth retaining structure, or structure designed to preserve or alter any natural feature, and any other structure similar to the foregoing; or

- any formwork, falsework, scaffold or other structure designed or used to provide support or means of access during construction work; or

- any fixed plant in respect of work which is installation, commissioning, de-commissioning or dismantling and where any such work involves a risk of a person falling more than 2 metres.

References and background information

HSC *Managing construction for health and safety* Construction (Design and Management) Regulations 1994 Approved Code of Practice L54 HSE Books 1995 ISBN 0 7176 0792 5

HSC *A guide to managing health and safety in construction* HSE Books 1995 ISBN 0 7176 0755 0

HSE *Health and safety for small construction sites* HS(G)130 HSE Books 1995 ISBN 0 7176 0806 9

Department of Transport *Safety at street works and road works: A Code of Practice* HMSO 1992 ISBN 0 11 551144 X

HSE *Dust and noise in the construction process* Ferguson, I. Contract Research Report 73 HSE Books 1995 ISBN 0 7176 0768 2

HSE *Information on site safety for designers of smaller building projects* Bone, S. Contract Research Report 72 HSE Books 1995 ISBN 0 7176 0777 1

HSE *Brief for a designer's handbook* Delves, A; Jofeh, C. Contract Research Report 71 HSE Books 1995 ISBN 0 7176 0896 4

HSE *The costs of accidents at work* HSE Books 1993 HS(G)96 ISBN 0 7176 0439 X

HSE *A step-by-step guide to COSHH assessment* HS(G)97 HSE Books 1993 ISBN 0 11 886379 7

HSE *Seven steps to successful substitution of hazardous substances* HS(G)110 HSE Books 1994 ISBN 0 7176 0695 3

HSE *General access scaffolds* GS 15 HSE Books 1982 ISBN 0 11 883545 9

HSE *Deadly maintenance: Roofs: A study of fatal accidents at work* HSE Books 1985 ISBN 0 11 883804 0

HSE *Deadly maintenance: A study of fatal accidents at work* HSE Books 1985 ISBN 0 11 883806 7

HSC *The control of substances hazardous to health in the construction industry* HSE Books 1989 ISBN 0 11 885526 3

HSE *Dust: General principles of protection* EH 44 (rev) HSE Books 1991 ISBN 0 11 885595 6

HSE *Occupational exposure limits* 1995 EH 40/95 HSE Books 1995 ISBN 0 7176 0876 X

Construction Industry Research and Information Association *Site safety: A handbook for young construction professionals*, Bielby, S.C., CIRIA special publication 90 1992 ISBN 0 86 017358 5

Construction Industry Research and Information Association *CDM Regulations: Case study guidance for designers: An interim report* Report 145 1995
ISBN 0 86017 421 2

Printed and published by the Health and Safety Executive   C100   3/95

Learning Resources
Centre

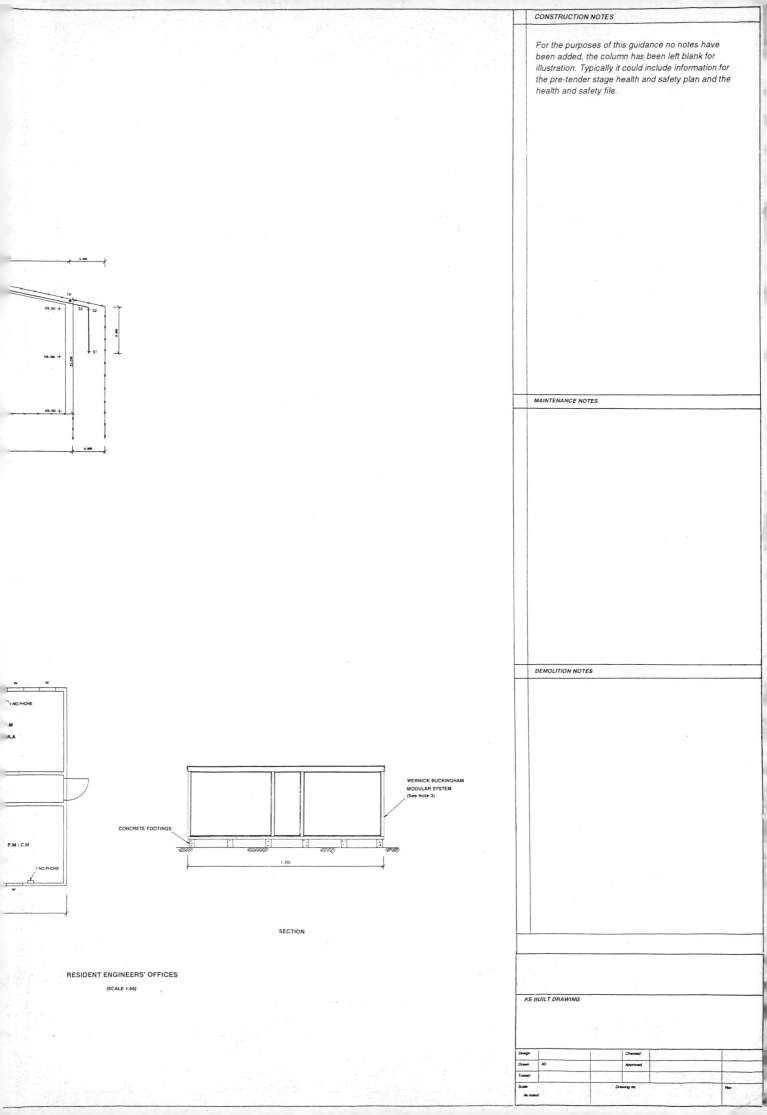

WERNICK BUCKINGHAM
MODULAR SYSTEM
(See Note 3)

CONCRETE FOOTINGS

7.300

SECTION

RESIDENT ENGINEERS' OFFICES

(SCALE 1:50)

1 NO.PHONE

.M

A.A

P.M / C.M

1 NO.PHONE

W

Design			Checked			
Drawn	AS		Approved			
Traced						
Scale			Drawing no.			Rev
As noted						

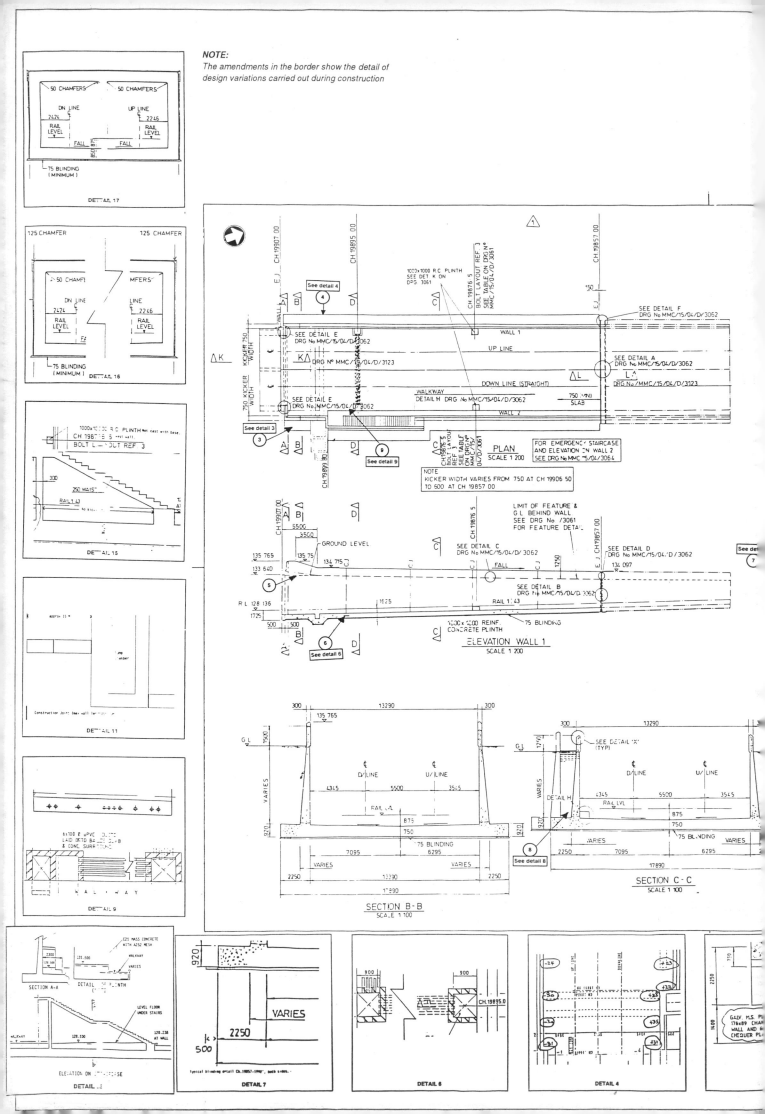

NOTE:
The amendments in the border show the detail of design variations carried out during construction

DETAIL 'Y'
SCALE 1:20

SECTION E-E
SCALE 1:20

See detail 1

See detail 11

See detail 15

Notes

1.

2 ALL LEVELS SHOWN ARE TO ORDNANCE DATUM (NEWLYN) + 100 m

3 THE REFERENCE ALIGNMENT HAS BEEN TAKEN AS THE CENTRE LINE OF THE DOWN LINE

4 CHAINAGES HAVE BEEN TAKEN ALONG THE REFERENCE ALIGNMENT

5 CONSTRUCTION JOINT (C J) EVERY 10 m IN WALL. EXPANSION JOINT (E J) WHERE SHOWN BASE & WALL

NOTES RELATING TO CONCRETE CONSTRUCTION

1 ALL REINFORCED CONCRETE TO BE GRADE C40 TO B.S 8110. MAX AGGREGATE SIZE 20mm U.N.O. [SULPHATE RESISTING CLASS 4]

2 BLINDING TO BE GRADE C25 MAX AGGREGATE SIZE 20mm [SULPHATE RESISTING CLASS 4] MIN THICKNESS 75mm

3 ALL EXPOSED FORMED SURFACES SHALL BE CLASS F3 BURIED TO BE CLASS F1
UNFORMED SURFACES SHALL BE –
- TOP OF FOUNDATIONS U1
- TOP OF WALL U3

4 KICKERS TO BE A MINIMUM OF 150 mm, CAST INTEGRAL WITH BASE SLAB

5 GENERALLY CONSTRUCTION TOLERANCES SHALL BE TO BS 5606 1978 EXCEPT AS NOTED BELOW:
- WALL POSITION IN PLAN ± 20 mm
- DIMENSION BETWEEN WALLS ± 30 mm

Reference Drawing

MMC/15/04/D/3020	GENERAL LAYOUT CH 15857 00 – CH 20440 00
MMC/15/04/D/3035	EXISTING SITE LAYOUT
MMC/15/04/D/3036	FINAL SITE LAYOUT
MMC/15/04/D/3041	SITE BOUNDARIES
MMC/15/04/D/3061	TYPICAL DETAILS SHEET 1 OF 2
MMC/15/04/D/3062	TYPICAL DETAILS SHEET 2 OF 2
MMC/15/04/D/3063	G A PLAN & SECTION CH 19907 00 – CH 19915 50
MMC/15/04/D/3064	G A WALL 2 & EMERGENCY STAIRCASE
MMC/15/04/D/3123	R C RETAINED CUT-SECTIONS

SECTION A-A
SCALE 1:100

See detail 17

See detail 16

SECTION D-D
SCALE 1:100

See detail 2

THE BASIS FOR SETTING OUT THE STRUCTURE IS DOCUMENT MMC/01/02/D/1506 "TRACK ALIGNMENT"

Rev	Date	Drawn	Description	Ch'k'd	App'd
1	AUG 93	G.H	TENDER, GRID REMOVED		
0	JUL 93		ISSUED FOR TENDER		

DESIGN VARIATION NOTES

(PLEASE NOTE ALL RELEVANT TOLERANCES FOR THE WORKS HAVE BEEN TAKEN INTO ACCOUNT)

17 50mm CHAMFER AS DETAILED ON DRWG.MMC/15/04/D/3063

16 125mm CHAMFER AS DETAILED ON DRWG.MMC/15/04/D/3063

15 PLINTH AND STAIRCASE STUB WALL KICKERS NOT CAST INTEGRALLY WITH SLAB

14 EMBEDDED TIES USED FOR F3 FINISH (REF.TQA No.35)

13 BLINDING CONCRETE GRADE C40 MAX.AGGREGATE SIZE 20mm TO BRE DIGEST 363 CLASS 4 (REF.SI No.16)

12 REINFORCED CONCRETE GRADE C40 MAX.AGGREGATE SIZE 20mm TO BRE DIGEST 363 CLASS 4 (REF.SI No.16)

11 CONSTRUCTION JOINT AROUND STAIRCASE WALL NOT AT 10m INTERVALS (REF.TQA No.33)

10 TRACK ALIGNMENT REVISED TO INCLUDE CO-ORDINATES AND LEVELS AT 1m SECTIONS

9 ADDITIONAL MANHOLE AND DUCTS WITH CONCRETE SURROUND (REF.DRWG.MMC/15/04/D/3028)

8 ADDITIONAL DUCTS AND MASS CONCRETE BENEATH STAIRCASE (REF.SI No.29 AND DRWG.MMC/15/04/D/3064)

7 BLINDING EXTENDS 500mm BEYOND EDGE OF BASE

6 6 No 100mm DUCTS (REF.CVI No.22 AND DRWG.MMC/15/04/D/3028)

5 CONSTRUCTION JOINT LEVEL MAINTAINED AT SAME RATE OF RISE AS THE REST OF THE WALL NORTH OF CH.19901.5 (REF.TQA No.79)

4 KICKER ALIGNMENT OUT OF SPECIFIED TOLERANCE BETWEEN CH.19895 - 19906 (0mm TO 35mm EAST) REF.TCL LETTER 11/07/94 CONTAINING NCR No.32 AND ASBUILT SURVEY

3 DETAIL AS DRWG.MMC/15/04/D/3028

2 ADDITIONAL THICKNESS OF BLINDING (300mm - 500mm) AT GRAVEL/CLAY HORIZON CH.19885 - 19895 (REF.RSM No.22)

1 20mm RECESS ADDED TO TOP OF FEATURE (REF.TQA No.43 & 51)

Design	A J D	Sep 90	Checked		5/6/12
Drawn	D J S	Sep 90	Approved		3/5/12
Traced					
Scale	AS NOTED		Drawing no		Rev 1

AS BUILT DRAWING

Design			Checked		
Drawn	AS	Sep 94	Approved		
Traced					
Scale	As noted		Drawing no		Rev 1

DETAIL 2

DETAIL 1

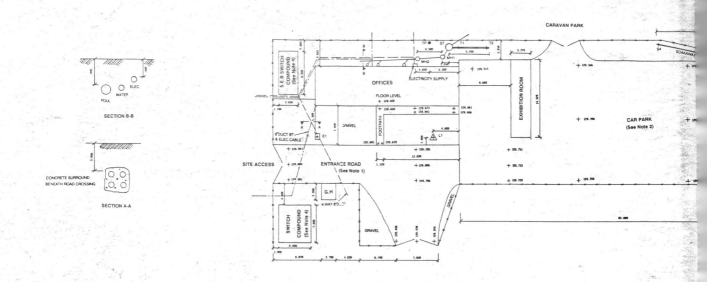

SECTION B-B

SECTION A-A

CONCRETE SURROUND
BENEATH ROAD CROSSING

COMPOUND AREA

(SCALE 1:250)

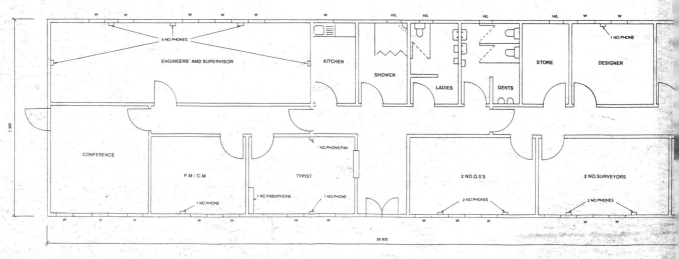

PLAN

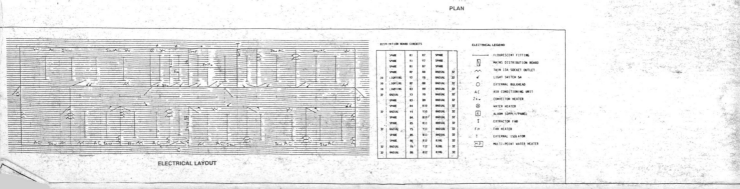

ELECTRICAL LAYOUT